Jaki Irvine is an artist who lives and works in Dublin and Mexico City. She is concerned with how we come to imagine and understand ourselves from within our privacy and often uses video installation as a way to reflect on moments where this process, awkwardly and unavoidably, comes spilling into the public spaces of our lives.

Days of Surrender is typeset in Mercury, by Hoefler & Frere-Jones. The titles are set in Besley's Two Line Grotesque.

DAYS OF SURRENDER

JAKI IRVINE

COPY PRESS

The Copy Press Limited
51 South Street
Ventnor
Isle of Wight
PO38 1NG

copypress.co.uk

Commune no. 6
Editor: Anne Tallentire
Reader: Yve Lomax
Copy-editor: Sara Peacock
Design: Amerang

Front cover and Frontispiece courtesy
of Kilmainham Gaol.
Group photograph in garden courtesy
of Bureau of Military History,
Military Archives, Cathal Brugha
Barracks.

Printed on Munken Print White
no.18 80gsm. Munken Print White
standard products are FSCTM
and PEFC certified.
Printed and bound in England.

First edition © Copy Press Ltd/
Jaki Irvine, 2013

Jaki Irvine asserts the moral right
to be identified as the author of
this work.

A catalogue record for this book is
available from the British Library

ISBN-13 978-0-9553792-8-4
ISBN-10 0-9553792-8-8

For my wife, my mother and sisters.

Photograph taken of the moment of surrender of 1916 Rising. The feet visible behind Padraig Pearse's in this image belong to Elizabeth O'Farrell.

Jesus. Sacred heart of Jesus. My heart. It's in my mouth.
Watching her there, with her handkerchief poking out the
door. Scrubbed and starched and stacked. One on hand for any
emergency. 'You can't go far wrong with that', we always say.
One flag out the window like a toe in the deep end, testing.
Tip tip tip. So far so good. And them opening the door with its
reluctant creak and their 'Go on, Lizzie. Go on now. Good girl.'
Like she's a horse. Look at her. I can't. Oh Jesus, Liz and Holy
Saint Anthony. Yes. Saint Anthony, I'm talking to you. Now.
Right now. Please don't let her be lost don't let her be lost ...
Not that. Are you listening? Not now, not now. Not when I
wouldn't let her say. Shushed her. Of all things, Julia. A shush
for Christ sakes! So alone out there. One foot in front of the
other. Laced up tight and everything pinned on the hankie,
so small it could be blown away any second. Oh Jesus Saint
Anthony don't let that get lost either.

I tried to do my bit: two red crosses — one for arm and apron
— willing them to be brighter and bigger. And the flag. A good
constrictor knot, that one. The starched white handkerchief
double tied for all it's worth. Strangling to death the bit of a
stick it is on. Damned hands nearly letting me down, betraying
me with the shakes. 'Steady as she goes', said Liz with a wink.
Could have been on the stage too. Ladies and Gentlemen, we'd
like to present the one and only Miss Elizabeth O'Farrell, coming
all the way from Holles Street Maternity Hospital for one night
only. One fine wink and a toss of her high head and they'd have
been eating out of the palm of her hand. Me shaking the blush
away as best I can. Always gets me that. She'd have given the
best of them a run for their money.

Ten years ago already, that night when we were running
through these very same lane-ways from the General Post Office.
The GPO not our headquarters then. Far from it. Little thinking
it could ever be such a thing. Quite the reverse. One side
of the thoroughfare crowded with the swing of Highlanders'
kilts and Redcoats as they were then and the girls up from the
country dazzled by the fit of them, by the young men with their
English accents inside. Dazzled into their own disaster, when
no respectable person would dream of walking on that side
of the street after nightfall. We'd seen some of these self-same
soldiers before, undoing their buckles to belt anyone who
looked crooked at them. Had the measure of them all right.
Our printed hand-bills hidden for the moment inside handbags
and muffs. *Irish Girls! Remember you are walking with your
country's enemies! You endanger your purity and honour!
We, Inghinidhi na hEireann, Daughters of Ireland ...* One of the
soldiers loud and abusive as he catches on, it spreading quicker
than the diseases we're trying to warn them about. *Remember
the Boers! Women and children starving in the camps!* This last
inserted at Madame Maud Gonne's insistence, she being the
president of our society. Always found it a bit confusing myself.
One thing at a time I'd say, but things being as they are,
'Your wish, as always Madame Gonne, is our command.'

A couple of policemen, they making their way towards us
through the crowd. 'You there! Missy!' And us taking to our
heels, light on our feet, swift and gleeful with the last of a cloud
of hand-bills flying up into the air, a printed flurry in our wake.
They cumbersome and bulky and finally puffing and dragged
to a standstill by the weight of their own overcoats. Liz giggling
and Helena Molony it was with us too, panting and laughing
when we finally got clear, ducking in behind the market walls
to catch our breath. Helena straightening bonnet and skirts.
She a friend of the great and the good, never mind her brush
with the law. Stone-throwing. Or rather, one stone thrown.
On the occasion of a royal visit. A portrait of King George

and Queen Mary its clear-sighted target. Glass broken. A case
of high jinks. The magistrate declaring that he 'would not brook
any Simon Tappertit, be they male or female'. And no, our Dear
Miss Molony would not countenance paying a penny. Indeed she
would rather be locked away. However, our heroine was released
unscathed from the hospitality of Mountjoy prison. Courtesy
of an anonymous benefactor. Due at the National Players Society
that particular evening. 'Sigh!' More theatrics. 'Although of
a more refined variety you understand!' Full of Yeats and Lady
Gregory's *Cathleen ni Houlihan* and wouldn't a journal for
women be a fine thing? 'Just imagine! Our own voices: Blood
and thunder!' Her carefully cultivated accent in keeping with
the slightly raised eyebrow. High thinking and home-made
bread. 'Why of course, Miss Molony, of course!' We watching,
amused, as she steps out onto the corner of Capel Street.
'Always a pleasure!' Setting off with a wave and a walk she's
been rehearsing these past few weeks.

And indeed you might walk me home Miss O'Farrell. Indeed you
might lend me your arm what with these uneven cobblestones
and indeed one could see no harm in that at all.

Oh Jesus, slow down now, Liz, that's right. Don't run or they'll
have ye. Steady as she goes. And the hankie's looking smaller and
smaller, bobbing and waving in the air above her head.

The cease-fire holds like bated breath. Eerie, the sound of a
piano jangling somewhere nearby. Hauled out through a broken
window and off with it.

British barricades up the top and bottom of the street.
We trapped like rats in between. Now Moore Street has become
No Man's Land. Oh Jesus. Liz in that empty desolate place.
Halfway out across it, disappearing with the angles growing
more acute from this broken slit of a window. Dirty bit of lace
curtain flapping in my face. They're shouting at the top of
the street from behind their barrels and bags of sand. Nosing
up against them with their rifles peeping out. What are they
shouting? Can't make it out. It's that young Tommy with the
moustache. I'm sure it's him. All talk about his Irish mother.
He couldn't take a currant bun from Liz and give her a hug all
friendly-like yesterday morning and shoot her dead on the spot
today, could he?

Mind you, he probably would all right if he'd realized what we'd
had under our aprons. Myself and Liz accompanied by little May
McLoughlin. Plucky as they come, that one. Gave her brother
Seán the deaf ear when he spotted her in the GPO. Told her to get
on home with herself, that she was too young and anyhow her
dinner was ready. It'd be done to a crisp.

Upstairs in the GPO Louise Gavan Duffy commands the
kitchens. Believing we don't have a hope in hell, she said
as much to Pearse when she arrived. However, in the meantime,
there's a job to be done. Women's League girls, *Cumann na
mBan*, they are for the most part. All work unstintingly. Jugs
of tea and sandwiches flying out the door. Taking turns to nap,
exhausted, under a table in the back room. A couple of Tommies
too, keeping themselves busy. One of them, a Dublin man,
cooking up a storm of sausages, cracking jokes with the girls.
Rosary beads swinging around his neck. Others washing up
alongside the women. Whistling. Proclaiming themselves very
well kept prisoners of war indeed. Wouldn't dream of escaping,
thanks very much. A bunch of British officers, quietly playing
bridge and sipping cups of tea despite the mayhem. One shifty-
looking fellow sulks in a corner.

Downstairs in the GPO a horse twitches, flicks its tail, tears
cabbage leaves from one of our Volunteers. May McLoughlin
keeps clear. Handed another dispatch. Warned by Joseph
Plunkett. 'If stopped: Eat it. Swallow it.' Kate Byrne on a similar
mission to the Four Courts. Inserts the message in between the
coils of her hair. Pink ribbon. Velvet hat firmly pinned on top,
securing the lot. Padraig Pearse and Joseph Plunkett smirking
at the sight. May too young to attract attention, slipping on
through, while myself and Liz are given the full treatment.
'Ladies, are you quite sure you want to be going up that end
of town? And why would that be?'

And no getting rid of him until Liz produced the currant bun
from one of her plentiful pockets and then with smiles all
round we were sent on our way, with a 'Well if you're both

sure then.' Across the barricades. Heel sinking into the worn upholstery of a sofa, catching on a tassel. 'Mind how you go. Watch your step. There you are. I shall of course. No bother at all.' Finally managing to unburden ourselves of both message and ammunition when we got as far as Commandant Mallin's outpost in Stephen's Green.

No Man's Land. The thought of it ferreting into our souls. Heard some of our lads have been there too, digging up the grass around the Green and burrowing themselves down into it, like they'd been doing it all their lives. Trenches in Flanders, full of rats and freezing cold, with all sorts of diseases running rampant. *Safer than the slums of Dublin*, or so goes the claim on the British recruiting poster, urging our young men to fight for the same king and class that has them living in such squalor. Not a trace of irony nor shame. And that old character not wanting to give up his cart. Sure who could blame him and it all that stands between himself and the workhouse. Stacked. Piled. Piano. Chairs. Dining table. Sideboard. Carpet rolled haphazardly. Bedsteads. Upturned. Upended. The cart lodged firmly in between other bits of recently commandeered furniture and him trying to break down their barricades to retrieve it. Still, he couldn't have been the sharpest knife in the drawer. Our Volunteers already starting to hide in behind it, shouting, 'You'll get it back when we're done. Go on out of that with yerself.' Him unrelenting. Tugging and agitating. Something comes loose with a crack. A growl. 'You've been warned. I won't tell you again.' Now there he is, lying like a spilt bucket in the dirt, with the cart fine, not a bother on it, and him with no use for it any more.

Reports of the Countess striding up and down around Stephen's Green, looking for all the world as if she was having the time of her life, practically unaware of the bullets whistling past and the British already lining up on the rooftops overhead. Those trenches finally doing no one any favours when the bullets start showering down on top of them from the machine gun mounted on the roof of the Shelbourne Hotel. Sitting ducks. Commandant Michael Mallin gives the order: 'Into the College of Surgeons. Tell the women. Retreat in twos and threes. Move! Now!' The open-air canteen and first-aid centre are suddenly abandoned. Nora O'Daly, losing her hat in the scramble, arrives flushed, breathless, irked by the notion that she might be misconstrued as one who gallivants around town bareheaded.

Miss Margaret Skinnider, skilled in gauging wind, light, velocity and distance. Pedalling against the odds on a borrowed bicycle. Dropping off messages and ammunition, mostly unnoticed in the chaos. Up on the roof of the Royal College of Surgeons, Miss Skinnider looks down her sights across the treetops of Stephen's Green. A figure in khaki keels over far below. A schoolteacher of mathematics in Glasgow over in Dublin on her Easter holidays. Frequent visitor to the hills around Dublin, testing detonators and the like. Training the Countess' Fianna. Inner-city boy scouts schooled in the art of marksmanship and explosive devices. No girls, no. The Countess professing herself confused by 'those dreadful girls'. They taunting her Fianna boys, leaving them tongue-tied and excited and slightly bewildered. A girls' scout group, *Clan na Gael*, is set up under other auspices. Captain May Kelly leads them down from the Dublin mountains. Proudly places them at the service of the Countess when they make it that far. Some of the younger ones only ten or eleven years old. They starting to cry in fright when they see what's afoot.

Margaret Skinnider finally arrives at the Countess' side. The unexpected thrill of a custom-made uniform laid out awaiting her arrival. Her presence unofficial but not unplanned. Moleskin. A beautiful material. To fight alongside the Countess. The soft chilling embrace of it. Miss Margaret Skinnider and Countess Markievicz. Well-designed handmade britches, belt and puttees for women. A most excellent markswoman, having learnt to shoot at a rifle club in defence of the British realm.

The .303 Lee-Enfield rifle: a heavy weapon with a strong recoil. Margaret Skinnider. Bits and pieces for detonators hidden in a bonnet. Wires in her skirts. News and urgent secrets on her tongue. Skidding around a corner as something hits and tears through metal and spokes and rubber. A hail of bullets rain down yet again from the roof of the Shelbourne. Maggie Skinnider. Dragged inside, writhing in agony. Moleskin and leatherwork ripped and shot through three times, the blood spilling out darkly, staining the material cruelly. Her hand held tightly in Madam's as Miss Madeline ffrench Mullen hunts and gouges for the bullets. Revenge, she is told at some point through the next feverish hours or days, lies in the form of an unarmed policeman the Countess personally shot dead, and she passes out of consciousness again with the cold comfort of this death hanging around her neck. Outside the College of Surgeons, one of our Volunteers sits on a park bench in the Green. Riddled with bullets. His arms spread out across the back of the bench looking as if he's taking the sun. Head leant back. Face crimson. Can't make out who he is for sure. So much blood. Collecting in a seeping puddle. Leaking, dripping from his fingertips, these twitching for an eternity. Faintly, hopelessly, noiselessly calling for help or respite. We none of us able to get to him.

Friday, 28 April 1916
Abbey Street

Sniper fire crackles.
Ricochets.
Ankle and shinbone shattered.
A gun clatters into the gutter.
James Connolly.
Dragged back inside.
Flesh lacerated.
Ether.
Machine-gun fire sweeping the streets outside.
Connolly unconscious.
Nurse Aoife de Burca keeps watch.

Friday, 28 April 1916
Inside the GPO

Fire begins to take hold, now that the water has been cut off.

Already some of women are gone, finding it impossible to get back through the lines after delivering their dispatches. More decide to chip in wherever they find themselves.

Christine O'Gorman, Brighid Foley, Mary Lawless, Phyllis Ryan and her sister Mary. She hell-bent on getting back to the GPO until a dog, crossing the path directly in front of her, drops dead at her feet, caught by a sniper's bullet.

Leslie Price to lead the first wave of women out under the Red Cross flag. Brigid Dixon and her sister Grainne, Tilly Simpson, Veronica Glasam, Annie O'Higgins, Stasia Toomey, Mary Adrine, Margaret Fagan, Mrs Mary Slavin, Mrs M.J. Rafferty, Bernie Richards, Eileen Murray, Brighid Lambert, Mrs Eilis Noone, Margaret and Josephine Walsh, Mary Hanley. Commandant Pearse and Seán MacDermott salute each one at the door. 'Chins up, ladies. Walk tall!'

Peggy Downy, a fine cook, stands conferring with her sister Francis. Over from Liverpool for the Rising, along with Nora Thornton and school teachers Kathleen Murphy and Kathleen Fleming. Announces she won't be leaving. Came here to give her all. Pearse demurs. 'Who is he to tell anyone they cannot fight for their country?'

Ammunition. Explosives.
Fire raging out of control, moving fast through the building.
Connolly wakes.
Seán McLoughlin, May's brother, twenty years of age sir.
'Prop me up, lad, prop me up.'
'Yessir.'
'Got to get out of here lad. Get us into Moore Street.'
'Yessir.'
Now Commandant McLoughlin, later told as the 'Boy
Commandant'.
Crowbars. Pickaxes.
Rubble.
Through the walls.

Kate Byrne crouching behind one balustrade and then another
as firing intensifies. Inching her way down the quays. Kate Byrne.
In and out of the Four Courts and the makeshift hospital in Father
Matthew's Hall. Red Cross Flag flying above it. Bullet holes in
her velvet beret. Close shaves. Sleeping on a sofa in one of the
tenements. Bread. Bandages. Sustenance. Endless tea for those
Volunteers manning the barricades. Sheets and bottles of spirits
torn and cracked open as the wounded are delivered here rather
than the nearby hospital. 'We're not going to surrender. We'll
fight 'til the last. Would you be game, Kate?' And she, 'Of course!
Whatever you do, I'll do.'

Kate taken to Monk's Bakery early Sunday morning. Volunteer
Mattie Gahan gives her a bag of bread. Her disguise. Her armour.
The whole lot tipped out onto the filthy ground as she attempts to
pass through British lines. Ten younger ones pounce on it all the
same, never mind the dirt of it, when she finally gets herself home.

Friday, 28 April 1916
O'Connell Street

The British cordon steadily tightens.

We arrive back to witness a hesitant runnel of misery, from the tenements of Moore Street and around, straggling under cover of a lop-sided white flag. A dismal procession of women and children, exposed and fearful, stumbling away from their homes like moles over the rubble. Out onto the blinding expanse of O'Connell Street.

And that skinny girl. Straggling behind. Terrified. Dropping to the ground at the slightest provocation. A stray horse, eyes wild – one of the many released or escaped from a stables nearby during the night – slips and skitters dangerously close to her head. Urged up to her feet and on again by a couple of the younger Tommies, shouting encouragement to her from across the barricades: 'Nowhere to go, sweetheart, but you'd best not stay there.'

Flames and smoke devour papers, timbers.

Christine Stafford Brooks, Molly Reynolds, Margaret Quinn, Mary O'Hanrahan, Brigid Connolly, Winifred Conway, Mary O'Reilly.
'Women and girls!'
Patricia Hoey, Máire English, Lucie Gethings, Bernie Richards, Eileen Murray, Máire Mapothar, Máire O'Neill, Lucy Smyth.
'Time to leave!'
Martha Murphy, Gertie Colley, Kathleen Murphy, Kathleen Kelly Barber, Áine Ni Riain, Margaret Fagan, Martha Walsh.
'All out!'
Mrs Mary Slavin, Louise Gavan Duffy, Nora Foley, Brigid Walsh, Louise Burke, Bridie Richards, Esther Wisely, Mrs Ellen Stynes.
'Yes! All of you!'
Cathleen Treston, Alice Byrne, Veronica Ui Glasam, Laura Daly O'Sullivan, Birdie Slater, Annie Tobin, Cathleen O'Reilly, Mary O'Connell, Annie O'Higgins, Peggy and Francis Downy, Aoife de Burca.
'Prisoners! You too! Go!'
'And the priest?'

This being one Father Flanagan. He initially reluctant to perform his duties when Leslie Price had first run, then finally crept from wall to wall, fingers moving like a blind woman's, clinging and edging brick to brick in and out of doorways and crevices towards the presbytery. Praising God for the command sent out to the women: No uniforms. Not so much as a pin. Attempting to crawl below the railings in Marlborough Street. Cursing the skirts that hamper her progress. Ignoring anxious shouts from hallways. 'Get in here out of the way! What on earth

could be worth it?' Pressing all the bells she can find. No answer.
Knocking then thumping and pounding against the silence of
the priest's door. Kicking and battering until he relents. 'Who's
there?' Opens up a crack. 'Murderers the lot of them. Let them
all burn in there.' And Leslie Price screws up her courage. Argues
with a priest for the first time in her life. 'Every last man and
woman in that Post Office is prepared to die, to meet their God.'

Father Flanagan's conscience is browbeaten into the street.
Eye-watering sunlight causing him to squint. Turning into
Moore Street, someone lies on the kerb, bleeding. Shot through.
Concentrating on breathing. On dying. The priest sniffs. Drink
taken. Refuses him last rites. Another. Head oddly angled against
a flagstone. White hair blown to one side. Bleeding onto the
ground, it pooling and sinking in the cracks. The priest recognizes
him. Eimer O'Duffy's father. Kneels to hear his confession. Leslie
Price unburdens herself of her charge at the GPO. Swallows her
disgust. Tom Clarke gives the order. 'On no account is the priest
to be let out.'

A beam creaks deafeningly and crashes in flames to the floor.
'And the priest?'
'Yes. Him too!'

All finally making a headlong dash for it.

Feet first. Falling through the walls of the GPO. Into the musty
blind embrace of the Coliseum. Nurses. Red Cross workers.
Cumann na mBan. A few Tommies switching sides, tumbling
through after them. Wounded men passed through last. Caught.
Stretchers. Bombarded, the building shudders and groans.
Everyone flat on the floor. Heads and heels. Huddled together in
this blacked out theatre. Trying to prepare for death in the pitch
black as bullets and bombs hammer the walls.

Friday, 28 April 1916
Parnell Monument, O'Connell Street

Attn. Staff Officer to General Lowe.
Sir,
A Lieutenant by the name of King reporting back, sir, having
escaped from the rebel Headquarters at the GPO. Padraic Pearse
badly wounded with a fractured thigh. James Connolly is dead.
The Countess Markievicz coming and going. A German Professor
makes bombs for them. Rebels adopt civilian clothes. They slip
undetected into the crowds.
R.L. Owens.
Lt. Col.

Friday, 28 April 1916
Henry Street and Jervis Street

In the lull that follows, a trail of women are sighted, awkward
and determined, moving under a Red Cross flag. Buildings blazing
all around. Scrambling over one British Barricade and then
another. Respectful of the Red Cross, grateful for them on the
battlefields of Flanders. Straggling on down the quays. Heading
for Jervis Street hospital, carrying the wounded in sheets, one at
each corner. Accompanied by a priest. British soldiers.

Volunteer John Kenny. He one of many delivered to the hospital
basement. A charnel house. Someone nearby heaves himself up.
'God Save Ireland' briefly bubbles on his lips. Ended by a rush of
blood. Volunteer Kenny passes out.

After a night lying on the hard floor of a hospital waiting room,
those women who have arrived from the rebels' headquarters are
released.

Friday, April 28 1916
Inside the GPO, 8.00 pm

Winifred Carney.
Secretary for James Connolly.
'Trust Miss Kearney as you would trust myself.'
'Yessir.'
Entered the GPO with Commandant Connolly on Easter
Monday, taking her trusty typewriter and Webley along with her.
'I'll be leaving the same way.'
'Just leave the gun, Winnie. Go on now.'
'I'll be coming with you, Sir.'
'I won't argue with you, Winnie.'
'I'll be coming with you, Sir.'
'Come on so, if you're coming.'
Smoke billows. Glass shatters. Explodes.
Every solid thing blown to pieces, crumbling in the furnace.

Moore Street. A street of smallholdings and tenements. More
chance of dying here than in the trenches. That family there.
They just couldn't believe it. Left it too late. Lying out there in
No Man's Land the lot of them. And the size of their flag. The
whole bloody bed sheet they'd taken to wave as if they were off
for a picnic. Filthy. But it must have been white at some point.
There was no telling him. And she tried. And the daughter tried.
After they wouldn't let us in. The old man, the granda'. Hiding
behind the door and them knocking outside and shouting and one
of our lads screaming in the road in his own blood. What did he
think he was playing at? No need to have his eye stuck up against
the keyhole to see that coming. And then there was nothing else
to do and that was that. We're in and he's still sitting there in his
armchair staring at the hole in the door and not seeing anything
at all nor any of us coming through it nor the shock on our faces
as we see him. And the screams still washing over all of us from
out in the street. Like watching a man drowning the way we
couldn't get to him no matter what, forced back against the walls,
watching him go under, until we shut the door and still it follows
us into the small parlour and we're all cold with the sound of it
seeping into us, making us feel sick and very far from home and
the old man's silence doing the same.

They were upstairs, the rest of the family. The father terrified,
pulling the sheet off the bed, with the mother flapping and
flustering around behind him trying to both help and hinder at
the same time. And Liz had given up on him, seeing as how he
was the spit of the oul'fella downstairs. The same mad blindness
about him. No way of seeing sense until it hits him in the head.
She was talking to the daughter now, slow and calm, the way
she does when the waters have already broken and she's telling

them to breathe, breathe, breathe and push and breathe and push and push and push and breathe, that's right. The slow floating solidity of it. And they'd cling to her voice for dear life, in the pain and the mess and the chaos of it all. And you can see the girl doing the same. Her eyes are wide with panic and she's licking her lips and listening, concentrating on what Liz is saying. That's the knack of her, ladies and gentlemen, the hush she lets fall over things as they become hers. Her own kind of hush that makes you feel everything is all right no matter what. 'There pet, there, that's right.'

But there's no time and this is not the time and Liz is telling her this. 'Do not go out there. Do not let him take you or your Ma out there. This is not the time. Tell your Da. Tell him, pet. Nobody's innocent here. There are no innocent bystanders in this house nor on this street. It doesn't matter any more who you say you are, not now. They're not listening. We're doing our best to get out of here. And then you might get out too. But right now you can't go out there. Tell your Da. Stay where you are. That's all there is to it.' And the girl. She's probably about fourteen, with more sense than the rest of them put together, and you can see the horror of it taking shape inside her and the panic turning into something heavy and dark and numbing as it sinks in and she's saying, 'Right, I'll talk to him I'll ...'

But there's no more time and we have to go and the screams are loud again as someone makes a dash for it and more banging and shouts and silence and then we're out and running and there's a roar and we're in.

Machine gun fire blasts the streets.
No going out.
Walls are broken through.
One into the other.
Plaster dust, bricks, rats, dirt.
Holes. Holes.

Bare feet scurrying, trying to get out of the way. A green-black stain creeping and crashing steadily upwards, leaving its trail of destruction. Small narrow houses full of corners, angles, stairs, cupboards, walls and people, people, people. Some of those who couldn't run or were afraid to, frozen to the spot as the walls came crashing in. Scuttling out of the way as best they can. Another door locked.

Mrs Margaret McKane further back in the house, listening to them tunnelling their way down the street throughout the night. Cooking up a bit of breakfast for them all when they get this far. 'Bridget, they're nearly here. Would you get the door, love?' Bridget McKane. Herself and her father. Rummaging, clinking, dropping the key in a panic. 'Open up now or we'll open it for you.' Fifteen she is. The key caught in the floorboards. Trying to work it loose. 'Stand clear in there, will you?' Mrs McKane keeping an eye on the potatoes. 'At least these will fill them up.' Volunteer Joe Good staring into the parlour. 'Oh Christ Almighty!' A piece of Bridget's skull on the ground beside her. 'Clean and white,' he mutters, dazed, 'like I'd imagine a baby's.' Picks it up and slips it into his pocket. 'So that no one will discover it.'

No. 11, T.F.Cogan, Confectionery
Morphia.
No. 13, Mrs Rose Anne Hogan
Morphia.
None.
No.
Gaping holes and rubble.
No. 14, Mrs Norton, China and Glassware
Gangrene.
Easing the stretcher on inside and over the top of a banisters. Jarring on something half-seen in a dim cramped kitchen. Crockery crashing to the floor and James Connolly roaring.
No. 15, Hanlon's Fishmongers

The stink of dead fish enough to turn the strongest of stomachs.
Connolly's infection spreading.
Silence.
Muffled thumps.
A groan.
No. 16, Mr Patk. Plunkett. Butchers, Poultry, Etc.
The stench of death already waiting there to greet them, subtle
but insistent, under bleached attempts to subdue it, sluice
it from heavy scrubbed wooden chopping blocks. Sacks of
woodchip and sodden sawdust slump in a corner.

Houses shelled. Succumbing. Collapsing in a deafening thunder.

Two things. Decisive things, as it were. One of them a 'Death or Glory Squad'. Seán McLoughlin's idea. Ready to hurtle headlong into their deaths, so that others might escape. An ardour both awe-inspiring and terrifying. A fragment of one of Pearse's own poems snags in his mind as he speaks with him. *Beautiful boy burning with passion.* 'Give me an hour, son, to think it over.'

And the other thing. It was Seán MacDermott who noticed them first. Called Pearse over to the window. We didn't know how long they'd been there like that, nor how we could have missed them. Machine-gun fire. Faster than you can say, 'One, Two, Three Elderly Gentlemen'. One still clutching a white flag. Bent stiffly together against the wall. And that broke it. Enough.

'It's our only hope. It'll have to be one of you', they're saying, looking from me to Julia. 'So that'll be me then.' As I couldn't live with myself otherwise. Wouldn't want to. Seán MacDermott sticking a flag out the window to see if it can stem the barrage.

More shots. One breath. In. Out.
A pause. Then another. In. Out. In. Out.
A shot. A roar. A silence.
All of us on tenterhooks.
'Don't know if it will hold.'
'Here, take this.'
The tremor in Julia's fingers. Distract her with a wink. Lightly does it.
'Julia ...'

'Shush now, shush!'
And I can't bear to look any longer. Coward that I am in front of
those ferocious unblinking eyes, she opening the door.

Carrying Commandant P.H. Pearse's message, this cargo of
cardboard and sadness and surrender. Under such a forlorn flag
and crosses. *Believing that the glorious stand ... has been sufficient*
... It was Julia who noticed the picture, thought it might do the
trick: a cardboard backing in behind the frame. A pencil. 'Where
would we be without art?' Her way of muttering that lets me
in and keeps everyone else outside of us. Now look at us, more
inside and outside than we ever dreamt of being. But this is not
the time. Steady as she goes. I won't look at more than their
feet now, sticking out across the cobbles. Six feet pulled from
underneath them and my own two crunching loud and heavy
across the glass. Slowly, slowly does it. Can't afford a slip or it'll
rattle the lot of them. *Desirous of preventing further slaughter* ...
That cockney lad with the Irish mother. If he's in behind there
he'll know me for sure.

The O'Rahilly's revolver over there. Sure of course it is and
his hat there too, flapping in the gutter beside it. Him forever
singing and whistling. You'd know he was on his way up the
stairs long before you'd clap eyes on him. Took thirty or more
of our lads out with him. A charge towards the barricades.
Oh Christ almighty! No, not now. Keep going. Look where
you're heading. But he must have gotten in somewhere after
all. They must have pulled him in after his plan turned into
a bloodbath.

They're shouting now, running around up there behind the
sandbags. 'All right, lads, all right!' Steady on there, Liz. That's
Julia in there. 'Sheila', she says. Loves the ring of her name in
Irish, 'Sheila Sheila Sheila ní Ghrianán'. I'm so sorry, love.
To open negotiations with the British commander... One foot and
then another. Breathe. Breathe. That's right: in out in out. Nearly

there now. Get them out. Get her out. Alive. Let her out or you'll be burying me alive too. 'Yes! Yes, it is! Nurse Elizabeth O'Farrell.'

Saturday, 29 April 1919
16 Moore Street
Mr Patk. Plunkett. Butchers, Poultry, etc.

James Connolly lying on the floor in the middle of the parlour.

Bodies all around.
A shifting of petticoats and boots near his head.
Later, it must be later, in a back room now.
Calls her close.
Julia leaning down into his fever.
'Don't be crying for your friend. They may blindfold her, take her across the lines. She may be some time. But they won't shoot her.'

And she's ashamed, hand up to her face, burning wet despite herself in the gloom that hides nothing. Face to her hand. Burning for her despite herself. Still struggling with it. Bows her head with thanks all the same. Holding onto these words like a rope as his infection continues to rage upwards unchecked. Telling them to herself bead by bead by bead until they are the rhythm she walks to through these tightening rooms.

Almost got you out. Almost. They were halfway through sending
me back. 'Women? Another two of them is there? Tell them
they'd better get out of there now if they know what's good for
them', he said.
'Right so, I will so.'
One foot back through the barricades when he changed his
mind.
'On second thoughts', he said. 'Best wait for the commanding
officer. Wouldn't want to jump the gun now would we?'

Oh Julia. I nearly had you out. Locked up in Tom Clarke's shop
instead, the British using it as a kind of headquarters. Seeing as
how Mr Tom Clarke is currently unavailable. Seeing as how the
Fenian bastard is in Moore Street consorting with a shower of
rebels. Seeing as how he'll never learn, not even after spending
fifteen years being taught the hard way in Portland Penitentiary.
And the papers: *Nationality, Workers Republic, Honesty*. Taken
off the shelves, flicked into my face. 'I suppose you know this rag
as well?' Lieutenant Owens. A surly character. Steps in all the
same when they start getting a bit out of hand.

Saturday, 29 April 1919
Parnell Monument, O'Connell Street, 12.10 pm

Attn. Staff Officer to General Lowe.
Sir,
A Red Cross Nurse of the enemy has come in with a verbal
message from the self-called Commandant Pearse, Republican
Force, to the effect that he wishes to treat with the Commandant
of the Forces. We have detained the nurse here and are
proceeding with the operation of searching and closing in.
Lt. Col. R.L. Owens

British troops under heavy gunfire. Ordered to tunnel their
way through the buildings. The mounting frustration of bricks
and mould, walls, vermin, squalor. Baying for blood by the time
they've made their laborious way to the end of the street only to
find the damned Irish rebels have slipped through their fingers.
Determined to have their pound of flesh. Rounding up all the
boys and men they can find. James Healy. Tom Hickey and his
son Chris. Hadn't wanted any part in it. Better off staying at
home, lad. Bullets. Bayonets when those ran out. Pounding on
the door of Ellen Walsh's house. Pulling her husband out onto
the street. No one innocent here. Paddy Bealen dragged out.
A woman arguing. 'Why can't you let him off? You know he
hasn't done anything.' 'I'd like to but I can't. They've seen him.
The officers. That's all there is to it.' Helped him say his prayers
then. Couldn't look him straight in the face all the same when
it came to it. Had him go down the rickety stairs. Fifteen bodies
found, all told. Two of them buried in a cellar.

Saturday, 29 April 1916
Parnell Monument, O'Connell Street, 12.45 pm

Upon arrival of Colonel Portall, Miss Elizabeth O'Farrell repeats her message: 'The Commandant of the Irish Republican Army wishes to treat with the commandant of the British forces in Ireland.'
'The Sinn Feiners you mean.'
'No, the Irish Republican Army they call themselves and a very good name it is too.'
'Damned spy!'
'Search her.'

Bread
Cakes
A handful of sweets
Two pairs of scissors

'Can Pearse be moved on a stretcher?'
'Commandant Pearse doesn't need a stretcher.'
'We have information to the contrary.'
'Commandant Pearse does not need a stretcher.'
'You think you can say anything you like, being a woman. Just watch out you don't find a shot through that pretty head of yours. Spy!'

Lieutenant Royall cuts the Red Cross off arm and apron both.

Saturday, 29 April 1916
Top of Moore Street, 2.25 pm

Brigadier General Lowe sent her back, watched her looking
further down Sackville Place than she had previously dared,
looking but not pausing, past a hat lying in the gutter and the dead
body of the O'Rahilly, his feet pressed against a closed door as if
he were somehow running still, his head dangling awkwardly off
the kerbstone.

'Half an hour and not a minute more. An Unconditional Surrender.'

Saturday, 29 April 1916
15 Moore Street

There is no time, no time, quickly delivered messages, backwards and forwards, slips of paper, unseen words scribbled in haste, grunts accompanying the reading, backwards and forwards, the urgent pressing of her warm rosary beads into my hands. 'Julia.' 'Tell him ... Tell him ... and Mr Connolly follows on a stretcher.' The door slams shut.

Time stretches out, walking down the road towards the end of it.

Brigadier General Lowe. 'Excuse me, indeed we are not late, Sir.
No, not one minute over. We are in fact exactly on time.' Pulling
back my overcoat to reveal my watch then, it pinned on so proud
and high, with its fine second hand ticking softly softly, loud
when nothing else is to be heard. *For Liz.* Elegant and solid,
the delicate precision of its movement a thing to count on.
The things we won't let go of no matter what. The officer behind
him, a Captain Wheeler. His son, I believe. Pulling his own
time-piece out of his pocket, to set it again by mine. Diverting
his smirk into the acceptable face of good time-keeping.

Commandant Pearse removing his weapons. 'Slowly, Sir. Slowly.'
The revolver and sword unclipped unhooked from their leather
holsters. His Volunteer jacket denuded in the process.

It was then I noticed him, that Tommy, setting up for the
photograph. 'Hold it there. Three. Two.' I stepped back. 'One!'
To spite him. Click. To not give him the satisfaction of making
that photo with me in it. I am aware that the Countess,
doubtless, would have done otherwise. That others in such a
moment, would have looked posterity more directly in the eye.
But not Elizabeth O'Farrell. Unwilling to claim this wretched
limelight. Stepped in behind Padraig H. Pearse and forgot about
my feet that were left sticking out behind his. My apron, my
overcoat. Stepped in behind Pearse and halfway out of history.
Stepped in. Stepped out. I would undo it if I could. I will regret
it forever.

Saturday, 29 April 1916
16 Moore Street, 3.30 pm

All of us on our knees then. Those of us who are left, those of us who can, propped up between rifles and rosary beads and the low sombre hum of a final decade and 'Oh my Jesus forgive us our sins, save us from the fires of hell.'

The shabby weight of cardboard replaced by typewritten orders and copies of orders. *Carrying a white flag proceed down Moore St ... March to within a hundred yards ...* All of us lining up under the command of Seán O'Loughlin before he falls into line beside us, disappears the way Connolly told him to. 'Youth not a thing to hand over, but to hold over for the future when he'll be needed for sure.' And Mr Connolly follows on a stretcher, disappearing through the gaping holes in the wall.

Saturday, 29 April 1916
Moore Street and Henry Street, 3.40 pm

Easy does it, easy does it. Seven of them it takes. A dead weight.
A roar. 'Christ will you watch it ye blackguard?' Struggling
against his own self, the gangrene rapidly gaining ground.
Manoeuvred from stretcher to stark hospital bed inside Dublin
Castle. Connolly signs. *I agree to these conditions ... for the men
under my command.*

'Well, Miss O'Farrell? Will you do it?' Don't know if they will
accept it. Accept orders from such as myself. Orders to
surrender. Pearse's word. Written. Signed. Connolly's also
carefully worded, not to get beyond himself. To avoid offence.
For the men under my command ... Aware that there are others
who would not want to accept his authority. I looking from
General Lowe to Pearse. Studying their faces for a crack,
a reprieve. 'If you are sure you want me to do this?' 'I am.'
Pearse's word final. General Lowe nods curtly. Gives his word:
'On accomplishing this you will not be held, but given safe
convoy pass to your home.'

Later. Later. Having been turned back once, then sent out again,
this time accompanied by the priest met en route, one Father
Columbus of Church Street. He thinking he might be of service.
They're in the Four Courts, the nearest of our outposts, under
the command of Ned Daly. Carrying the orders as I was asked,
as I agreed, as I had no choice, as Julia is with them, marched
off up the street. Marched off with the rest of them. Me stopped
and passed and stopped and turned back at one barricade and
then another. Under no circumstances to be let pass and you
again and yes and on you go and Father. 'No thanks Father, I've
got nothing to confess.' Hands under her hair lifting it up off her
shoulders and the skin so shy and unexpectedly warm and pale
underneath. A shiver, slight and delicate. A quick glance and the
flicker of a smile like Morse code over her shoulder. Never told
her. Never said it. She never wanted to speak of it. Never wanted
me to mention it. 'No thanks, Father.' Nothing to be said. Lifting
and twisting, tucking it high and tight with those quick deft
hands pinning it firmly under her cap.

A cape for the shoulders. The Red Cross Brassard on both her own and Winnie's arm too for good measure. 'No harm in making sure, eh?' No harm at all. That's the way of her. As if things will fall apart if they're not secured and buttoned and fastened up tight and double knotted, a good square knot. Sure isn't she right? Where would we be without it? Where would I be? Fingering her rosary beads now walking down towards them, the gulls screaming high out over the river. *Those surrendering are warned that ...*

'I'm sorry, Ned, there's nothing else to do. I know. Tell our girls too. Those here under your command. Yes of course. And those in Father Matthews Hall.' They'll be hemmed in if they don't get out. 'We all know. They are for sure. Fine without doubt. Can't be done. I'm sorry. Tell them' ... *to lay down arms.*

Heavy machine-gun fire and constant rifle shooting. Mrs
Margaret Naylor is making a run for it, through thick crossfire.
Three children in tow. Her husband, Mr John Naylor of the
Dublin Fusiliers. 36 years of age. Killed by gas this same week on
the battlefields of France. The Naylor children are orphaned on
Rings End Drawbridge. The body of their mother lies out there
for days. Swept up in the chaos that follows. Its final resting
place unknown.

Maire Smartt hugs a heavy package. Food and ammunition.
Cautioned to halt at a British barricade. A sudden blast provides
the distraction she's praying for and she's off. Hesitates at the
sight of Margaret Naylor's body. A woman shouts out to her
from the cover of a nearby doorway. 'Don't be a fool. Get on
home with yourself. That poor woman's beyond help.' Maire
makes it to Boland's Mill. Greeted by a Volunteer who lowers
the insolent tip of his rifle. 'Here, hang it on the end of this.'
This she does. Ignores the insult of it. Offered no safe harbour,
nor the suggestion that she join them.

Saturday, 29 April 1916
Parnell Monument, O'Connell Street, 7.30 pm

Across from the Rotunda Hospital, our Red Crosses stripped
from us. Somehow naked and vulnerable in their wake, with the
jumbled heap of guns and ammunition piling up like another kind
of monument. Rifles, pouches, bayonets, bandoliers, leather cross
belts, bullets. Charles Stewart Parnell, the 'Uncrowned King of
Ireland', making his eternally grand speech up there, presiding over
all from his pedestal, with his bronze hand pointing to something
finer than this growing heap of weapons we're stacking up
underneath. Can't see it without thinking of his sister Anna. That
time she gave her talk. Frail and elderly by then. Intensely quiet.
Or was it impassive? What was it? A steeliness about her that was
almost repellent. And yet there was something queerly attractive
about her for all of that. A fine looking woman in her hey-day.

And Francis Sheefy-Skeffington thinking to catch her out with
his question about the treaty, expecting her to defend or excuse
her brother. The long cold stare she gave him would have chilled
anyone to the bone, not to mention when she answered that,
on finding himself in an awkward situation, her brother 'did
what any man would have done: found the most convenient way
out of it for himself, without a thought of the consequences for
anyone else.' The look on Sheefy-Skeffington's face. 'Floored',
he declared himself to be, chatting with myself and Liz afterwards.
His wife Hannah in and out of the GPO all this past week looking
for him. He, like her, a dedicated pacifist and suffragist. Took
her name on marriage and added it to his own. Unheard of. She
taking parcels of food here and there as a favour to us, ammunition
too, despite her reservations. None of us able to shed light on his
disappearance. Last seen setting off in an effort to stem the
tidal wave of lootings with a sheaf of leaflets. Such fine high-
falutin' foolhardiness.

What's that smell? Burnt sardines. Of course. The revolvers.
Stinking they are. No engine oil to keep the guns and rifles cool.
They jamming when overheated. Used whatever was to hand.
Tins of sardines and the oil they were in.

They're taking down names. Making a list of us. Names,
addresses, ages. Only one fella nearby isn't asked a thing.
The officer just looks at him long and hard and moves on to
the next. 'Ah, that's me brother', he shrugs. Then they're taking
the younger ones out and just like that nobody's talking nor
whispering nor barely even breathing and there's a tension
buzzing in the air. Captain something or other. British officer
he might be, but definitely a Dub, probably a Fusilier. Calls crisp
and clear: 'Seán Harling, Seán Harling. Out. Here. Now.' And you
could cut the air with a knife. 'Now, if you know what's good for
you.' He's about sixteen or so. Seán. Stepping out, he gets a clip
on the ear and is told to get on home to his mammy with himself
and all of the other boyos in that line too. None of them budge.
This finally bellowed out – a fine pair of lungs on that one –
until the shamed shuffle of the young lads begins, they moving
and dispersing slowly, then ever faster down the shell-shocked
street, like sleepwalkers who've been jolted awake and don't
yet believe it. Not dead. Neither jailed nor on their way to the
colonies. Seán McLoughlin in with them.

It was a Fusilier too up around Stephen's Green. Full of swagger
and madness, saying how he was for no one and no one could
touch him. And maybe they couldn't but they riddled him with
bullets all the same, so that he finally folded over onto the
ground. Not so sure if it was our side or theirs that did it.

By the end of it they say they were shooting their own shadows
this past week, some of them stunned to find themselves wishing
to be back in the misery of the trenches, where everyone knows
who's who and what's what.

Two young girls they were, all done up in finery and silly with it. Fur coat, pink silk stockings, blue ribbons streaming from one of the bonnets, stepping out through the broken windows just before Clery's went up in flames. One of them was laughing and hooting, pointing something at them, across the lines. 'How d'yiz like us now?', when a short blast of bullets stopped them in their tracks. The young soldier had the same look of shock on his face as themselves, on finding it was a fan she'd been clicking and pointing at him. Flirting, foolish, giddy. The kind he'd have spent all his night screwing up his courage for, to finally ask tongue-tied for a dance. A Captain Gerrard it was, who took the gun all gentle-like out of his arms. 'Out of harm's way, lad', concentrating on the weapon all the while, trying not to look too hard in the dead eye of what will never be undone.

What does that fella over there think he's up to? Turning a hose on our lads and they already prone on the grass. Soaked to the skin. They'll catch their death. Put a uniform on some of them and they lose the run of themselves entirely. Tom Clarke caught up in it too. There's no need for that sort of carry on. His brother-in-law Ned put standing with him, naked and belittled, in the middle of the street. Stripped by some poor gobshite in khaki who thinks it's funny. 'Give us a good look at you, you Fenian bastard!' Parnell pointing out the error of his ways, his stiff bronze finger wagging at him from on high: 'Fool.' The nurses looking out of the Rotunda too. Shaking their heads and no wonder. Captain Lee Wilson signing his own death warrant in front of so many and nothing to be done about it. Captain Lee Wilson. Too many eyes. Until he picks it up on the wind, the chill of it accusing him, marking him, memorizing him from all sides, his own name like a death sentence now and no one to blame but himself. We're all put lying down, nose to the gutter, thanking you, Captain Lee Wilson, to the grass and the dirt. The cold, damp smell of it.

To think that no matter how much he argued, Parnell fell off his pedestal in the end, undone by the love of a woman too. Undone too. That's what I'm thinking and I'd rather not be thinking it. Lined up alongside one another like sardines. The men put lying on top of one another. Some of the Volunteers haven't had a proper bite to eat in days. Liam Tannam boasting of the fine meal he made out of a raw egg and a square of Chivers jelly. One of our lads spotted chewing an Oxo cube. Taken out and stripped again for good measure. Bloody starving. A howl as someone's foot is cracked with a rifle butt. 'That'll teach you to stick out of line.' Groaning and complaining but definitely keeping a bit warmer huddled up on top of one another, that's for sure.

Jesus, it's bitter. I'd do it all again if you could only undo me once more. Warm me up and undo me button by button by button and warm me up and Jesus I'm freezing. What am I thinking? Undone, unstuck, unravelling, teeth chattering. I beg the Lord my soul to keep. Winnie Carney here too, shivering and praying and fretting over James Connolly. Overheard them in the back room. She wishing for some last minute glimmer of hope. It was beyond him. 'No other way, no.' He left his coat with her. 'Here, you'll be needing this more than me.'

'Seán Mac Dermott. Joseph Plunkett. You have cripples in your army I see.' A lieutenant something or other it was, looking down at the men on the ground, until Seán replies clear as cut glass. 'You have your place and I have mine and you had better mind your own place.' I'd swear I saw his cheeks colour as he turned heel quick sharp and strutted off.

Winnie speaking low and urgent now, seeing both men in a severely weakened state and in dire need of proper attention. 'And no, she won't be taking no for an answer. Our Red Crosses may be stripped from our arms but that changes nothing so far as we're concerned.' She's taken it off now, Connolly's coat, and her own after it. His lying on the grass, with hers on top. As their nurse and comrade and, she would like to hope, some manner of friend, in the spirit of their good friend whose own coat lies with hers. Insisting, insisting. 'A little warmth and rest', until finally neither can resist any longer. Sure look, isn't she grand? And isn't Julia's coat here big enough for two or even three of us? And she looks at me, stricken, as they ease themselves down, under her coat, onto his.

Trying to put a brave face on it, but we saw them lift Connolly out. Seven of them it took to carry him, borne back through the holes in the walls on a stretcher. And the gangrene still at its foul work. His clarity of mind always and still an awe-inspiring thing. *If the worker is a slave of capitalist society then a woman is a slave of that slave …* What so would that make me? Never plucked up the courage to ask. No point asking for it, that's what I've always said. 'But who are we fighting for then, Julia, if we don't have the courage to fight for ourselves? And how can we do that if we don't know how to be ourselves?' 'Of course we're ourselves. Who else do you think we are?' 'Don't be acting it. You know what I mean.'

She thinking of Eva, the Countess' sister. Gone to live with Esther Roper in Manchester. Writing on suffrage and women's working conditions in the mills. Their new journal, *Urania*, to include essays and poems on Sappho and the love of like by like. Admirable indeed, Liz. But they have a safety net we will never have. We just can't afford it. No, love. Leave well enough alone. With my nose in the grass, we're a bit late to be having these arguments. A bit late for me to be climbing down off my high horse too. Oh Mother of God it's bitter.

Saturday, 29 April 1916
O'Connell Street, Parnell Monument
A boarding room above the National Bank, 11.15 pm

Lieutenant Royall told to keep a close eye on me but not regard me as a prisoner. Stationed outside my door all night.

I can't make out the faces from up here, just the ammunition and bodies piling up. The stench of cold and damp, our burnt city and dead bodies. *To prevent the further slaughter of Dublin citizens* ... What are they doing putting them lying out on that grass on such a night? They'll catch their death ... *saving the lives of our followers* ... A heavy pall ... *will order their commands to lay down arms* ... Smoke so heavy and thick, making of the dusk something solid, the darkness thickening around them, heaving itself down onto them. Still sporadic shooting. Snipers. The odd flare. Every now and then the blast of what must be a grenade. Now darkness. *Surrenders will be accepted at the following places* ... Oh Julia, is that you down there? You'll be perished.

Captain Wheeler. Waiting halfway down the street in his car.
Empty, but for the sniper fire whistling past sporadically, it being
early morning. A dead horse lying bloated near the entrance to
the Green. Wheels of the cab it must have pulled sticking out from
the barricades. Me shaking with tension, waiting to be sighted.
Walking into the very place we brought ammunition and food to
a few days ago, knowing I carry something more unpleasant, most
unwelcome, the very act of delivery itself almost having a whiff of
treachery about it. This clinging to me, seeping through the page,
faintly staining me by association. Julia's beads clicking together
at every step. Click. Step. Click. Step. Winding them through my
fingers. Holding me to her. To myself. Inching forward. A hand
briefly framed in a broken window. Waves me on. Disappears.
A couple of little gurriers, dirty bare feet, dart into the bushes for
the thrill of it. Dodging bullets. Not believing they might get cut
down by one of them. Dashing out again as quick. Target practice.
Lad of the grey eyes, that flush in thy cheek ... Ah, Mr Pearse, what
a thing that poem of yours. It certainly strikes a peculiar kind of
chord all said. *Child of the soft red mouth ... A fragrance in your
kiss that I have not found yet in the kisses of women or in the honey
of their bodies.*

That two-year-old down in Church Street. 'Foster', they said,
John or Joe, I didn't quite catch it. Lieutenant Royall and a couple
of the others muttering before we set off in the car. Shot in the
head. No honour nor anything close to it in that. Not for any of us.

Inside the Royal College of Surgeons. Madeline french Mullen.
The love of Dr Kathleen Lynn's life this many long year
Disconcerted. The Countess and Commandant Mallin are asleep
I'm told, she reluctant to wake them. A long night ... Nothing

for it but to insist, persist. Order. Commandant Mallin. No, it cannot wait. Yes. Disturb him. Right now. The unanticipated shift in roles. Madeline alarmed by the tone of it, by the fact of it. Uncompromising. Unconditional. The squeal of a hinge, the turn of a doorknob and she re-emerges from the gloom accompanied by the Countess. Odd to see her off-guard like that, before full wakefulness is upon her, hesitating in the doorway, at the sight of me.

We with Connolly so many times in Liberty Hall. Not to mention our dear Helena Molony, whose charm opens doors others find barred. She lodging with Dr Lynn and Miss ffrench Mullen these past months. Yet it appears that nothing will bridge the unspoken moats encircling some of these women. An instance, nothing more, and she is quite herself again. Second-in-command to Commander Michael Mallin. Lieutenant . Her standing here as elsewhere assured by the very same sense of entitlement that our Rising is trying to undo.

Will we never be done with it? Never take our place in the world. On an equal footing with all, fit to look anyone in the eye. That's what our proclamation sets out. Black ink never looked so fine to my eyes. And from a certain distance, you'd imagine Madam's a figurehead for all of us. She, like so many others calling for suffrage, if only on behalf of those women with property. 'One thing at a time', they say and, 'one thing at a time', says Julia. The thin end of the wedge. Never mind that the filter through which these long-awaited rights might trickle further down has been woven disturbingly tight and is jealously guarded. Perhaps an unforeseen tear might occur in the filter, as it rips apart from British rule, an opportunity to seize upon, like coins dropped unnoticed during a skirmish.

Still, so many of the women worship her. Honoured by her presence, they delight in her eccentricities of character and upbringing, protecting her fiercely. And very few too, those who would dare to gainsay her. 'Petty.' That's what Helena calls my misgivings. And who knows. Maybe she's right. How tangled the thing is.

This the same outfit, complete with feathers in the hat, modelled some weeks earlier at the Keogh Brothers photographic studios. The Countess leaning on a fallen pedestal. Mallin's cast-off jacket fitting her like a well-made glove, he being a slim build of a man. Some Greek temple or other, painted into the backdrop. One eye on posterity, the other on the revolver in her hand. History, like beauty, being in the eye of the beholder.

That night in Liberty Hall. All of us gathering there in preparation for the events to come. The Countess unhooking her skirt in a backroom to reveal her bespoke breeches. Thrilled with herself. Me thrown off course, unsettled by Madam's childish excitement with her costume in anticipation of what could only be imminent carnage. Julia catching me then. Quietly setting down the first aid kit, her small hand laid firm and strong over mine. 'Here, roll this bandage for me, there's another hundred or so still to go.' We hoping against hope that all can rise on the same tide, that there will prove to be something else, something better, beyond the theatrics of bloodshed and glory, that other possibilities might reveal themselves through the upheaval.

That night lying in the still before the storm, feeling Julia's breath warm on my neck, the weight of her arm, listening to her whisper, 'Maybe it's not one Rising but many, like different drops of water coming together in a tidal wave.'

Now Michael Mallin's at his Lieutenant's side. He, then both, grimly studying the orders I have brought. The finality of it draining the colour from their faces. Mallin most certainly reading his death sentence. Composes himself. Quietly takes command of the situation. 'We will all breakfast first, before making mention of this.' All living on the most meagre rations this past week. God knows when the next meal might be. It hangs in the air, unsaid. 'Hold them off, hold them off until we can break it to them.' I nod, turning towards the door.

Talk of moving Maggie Skinnider to hospital, she being gravely wounded.

Sunday, 30 April 1916
Grafton Street

'What did Mallin say?'
This from Captain Wheeler.
'Nothing.'
'You should have insisted on a reply, had him state his intentions to comply.'
'He said nothing.'

Later a white flag is hoisted, flaps despondently over the Royal College of Surgeons. Murmuring as those left inside are rounded up. Necks craning. A few of our women mingle with the disgruntled crowd outside. Unnoticed. Disappearing. 'Nothing to be seen here. Move along!'

Still the horses lie enormous and bloated on the streets where
they fell. The shouting and jeering turns murderous as we pass.
Glad of an armed escort now. Women furious, some of them
looking like to tear us limb from limb, howling and hurling
even more abuse than the men. Army separation women,
a lot of them. Husbands and sons off fighting in the Great
War and them eking out some sort of living on what's left of
a queen's shilling per week. You'd be hard pushed to keep a
roof over your head on that, let alone feed a clatter of young
ones. Thinking if the empire sets them adrift they'll be sunk.

I've heard the same from Louise Gavan Duffy's landlady when
I came to call. Worrying about her husband losing his pension,
what with him being an ex-policeman. Martin. A great big
galoop of a man, and her a little bit of a thing. She could twist
him round her little finger if she wanted, but sure he's her life
and soul, she says. And even if she's delighted about the Rising,
the thought that he might lose his pension is nearly too much
for her.

Marching again, numb feet coming back to life as we fall in,
prisoners in our own streets and those in ruins around our ears.
Five days. Who'd have thought? Heaps of glass and rubble. The
windows of Clery's turned molten, melting, shattering in one
great wave, down onto the pavement. The terrified madness of
it sweeping up the street in a blind panic and stampede, people
running, falling, trampled to death.

Anne Caldwell lying amongst the dead horses, still reaching
after the hand of Mary Raymond as she was dragged away from
her and lost underfoot. Found afterwards, further up the street.

Some of them left lying there for days, sacks pulled over their heads for decency's sake.

In Corporation Street Buildings, Sarah Caffrey notices some activity out on the street. Turns to wipe her daughter's face. Two years old. 'There lovey, there.' A sharp pain as a bullet passes through Sarah's hand. Christina already dead when she is finally persuaded to take her hand away as if she could somehow hold the life into her. Stop it from pulsing out.

Names. Details. Hurled at us like blows, as curses upon our heads while we march.

And no, Mr MacDermott and Mr Plunkett ought not be walking. They don't have the strength for it. No more than that pair of oul' bowzies should be suffered to come with us. Too drunk to see they shouldn't be trying to fall in with a march towards a gaol. Where do they think they're off to? The worse hangover in many a long year if they don't clear on out of it now.

Barricades block the streets at every turn. Ours and theirs.
Captain Wheeler drives so far and stops. Afraid of being
ambushed. I am ordered out and across the firing lines. Alone.
To find Commandant Éamon de Valera. Reports that they were
on the move, into Boland's Mill and out again across the railway
bridges. Up in Westland Row, the British are lined up across the
top of the street, screaming at me to go back. I cannot. If I stop
I will sink, the way your boots fill up with water in Sandymount
and the only thing to do is to keep going, keep moving, not
get dragged under. Deceptive, how it sneaks in behind you
before you notice, cutting you off if you're not careful. Leaving
you stranded. How have I come so far adrift? Need to ask.
Their commandant. I can't feel the beads nor my watch. Oh
Jesus, love, I'm sorry. What are they doing with you? Lying all
night out on that damp grass. Frozen solid. Waving my white
flag and the paper at them and they screaming screeling like
gulls that would skewer me now with their bayonets were they
given the go-ahead. Then, despite their reluctance, I'm past
them, stumbling clear into the emptied streets.

Someone hesitates for a minute in the shadows. Makes a
break for it, a bottle of milk in hand. Volunteers are firing
from up above in the gasometer. Knocking and calling up at
the gasworks. The Old Distillery. Nothing. No one. Despite
what the other fellas told me. Outside Boland's Mill. Two loaves
of bread and a woman's hat lying on the ground in a drying
puddle of blood. Calling. Shouting. Growing hoarse with it.
Nothing. Except the banging and whizzing of bullets. Crossing
Grand Canal Street Bridge and you wouldn't hear anything
above the din.

The barrage terrifying. The smell of it thick in the air. Eyes
streaming. Can't go back. Waving high the flag and paper. That's
it. Breathe now. Steady as she goes. You can do this Elizabeth
O'Farrell. You can do this. A loud blast from somewhere out
of sight and a thud directly behind me. Not two feet away, a
middle-aged man drops bloody to the ground. 'You're all right,
you'll be all right. Can somebody please? Now?' Already the
ground blackening around him. 'Minding me own business', he
says. What a place to be minding it, I'm thinking, but saying,
'You'll be all right. You're all right.' Holding, shouting, until a
few people come running out. 'Easy now, easy.' Carrying him
away like a corpse between the lot of them.

Cats. Mangy and wild-eyed. Ribs sticking out through matted
fur. All manner of markings and sizes. Roaming the streets.
Perched on top of walls. Squeezed between gaps in the rubble.
Staring unblinking as I pass. Bizarre, so many. Rats too. Skulking
by walls. Rustling in bedraggled bushes. One brazenly sits there
watching me. Enormous. Thank Christ for a couple of our lads
who recognize me. It was the cages, they're telling me. In the
Cat's Refuge. Left them open. Only thing to do.

Leading me around the back of a building. The Dispensary.
Barricades removed with a low hollow grunt and squeal of nails
and wood. Having scuffled and scrambled awkwardly through
the bared window, I am greeted stiffly by Mr Éamon de Valera.

Something off. Right there and then I can't figure it out. Only
later it occurs to me. No women in this outpost. A mix-up, some
of them say, when I ask about it.

But back to Mr de Valera. Commandant. He eying me up and
down with suspicion, refusing to take my words as trustworthy
nor the authority of the signed papers I hold as my witness
and proof. 'A hoax', he declares, until the Volunteers vouch for
me in no uncertain terms. And then, 'I will not take any orders

except from my immediate superior officer.' And that'll never be from a woman as far as he's concerned. This despite Pearse and Connolly's signatures.

Has he not read the proclamation at all? *Equal rights and equal opportunities … oblivious of the differences carefully fostered …* Does he not know what we're fighting for? *Suffrages of all her men and women …* Has he no idea why so many women are fighting? What's he thinking at all? Is that why we've learnt to shoot as good as any of them? For the chance to make a better cup of tea? Captain Rose MacNamara under no illusions. Commands her girls to report to the GPO if for some reason they find themselves unable to fight alongside Commandant de Valera's men. 'Unmanageable', he says of us. And sure doesn't that say it all? Mr Éamon de Valera. It would appear, sir, that we've been fighting for different futures in different Irelands this past week.

All left unsaid, hanging in the air as I set off again, back through the shooting and ruins, across the other side of the city, looking for Commandant Tom MacDonagh.

James Plunkett unable to walk. Fainted on the way. Caught sight of him for an instant before he was bundled away.

Specially readied for us indeed. Not suitable for man nor beast this past ten years, yet here we are, in the decommissioned section of the building. Dirt and squalor. This, the oldest wing of the building, in a most serious state of disrepair. Felt the cold air hit me like a slap when we were marched in. Limestone. That's what does it. Soaking up the moisture from the air outside and releasing it into our cells, into our bones. Freezing. Dark. Shivering.

Names given in Irish much to the consternation of those soldiers tasked with the writing of them until they have enough of 'this codswallop' and begin writing English versions of our names despite the protests.

The British military in command here, but we stripped by two women warders brought over from Mountjoy Gaol. One of them a right scourge, years of chivvying poor unfortunates having clearly left their own scars on her personality.

Skilly shoved at us for supper. A sloppy grey swill. Mess tins sliding along the floor to us. No spoons. Left to eat and drink as best we can. All in the same mess tins. Wouldn't know what'd be in it, what you'd catch. One basin of murky water. A bit of bandage and a handkerchief as a towel. The lock of the door clangs heavy and final. Eyehole blocked. Bolted, barred. Three dirty threadbare blankets between four of us. Thick with lice and fleas. Scratching half the night. At least there's a window. A patch of sky.

Murmuring. Commending our souls to the Almighty through these hours of darkness. Oh Sweet Jesus, if it be your will protect her, Lord. Let her come to no harm, I pray. If we are suffered to live through this I will not let her leave my side again, neither in this life nor the next. Even if we are the only two women to lie in the ground together when our time comes, so let it be.

Don't let her be lost. Don't let her be lost.

Bleak beyond belief.

Sunday, 30 April 1916
15 Peter Street
Jacob's Biscuit Factory

Miss Christina Caffrey, dressed in widow's weeds, a Dublin
Fusiliers' emblem in her coat, passed through the British lines
with a 'mind how you go Ma'am.' Passed from one garrison
to another. A request for help rolled up small and tight in her
mouth. Too late. Too late.

May McLoughlin has already been and gone. Dressed in blue
overalls from the factory to cover her uniform. A message if she
makes it back to the GPO: 'Yellow Bittern. Yellow Bittern.' Louise
Gavan Duffy, Peggy Downy, turning up after escaping the GPO
to accompany Lily Murray home. Such a pretty, flighty young
thing that she would surely get herself into trouble otherwise.
Others too. Sarah Kealy, Kathleen Lane, Eileen Conroy. Arms
and grenades. Eily O'Hanrahan given orders: get rid of them
before the inevitable raid. Her sister waiting outside. Terrified
of getting torn to bits by the mob of women in the street. Máire
Ni Shiubhlaigh, actress, is the last woman to leave Jacobs.

Young Martin Walton, earlier in the week, trying to get in, with
that shower gathering around him at the door. Mary Neil, a
big-boned hardy woman asking what did he think he was up to,
joining a bunch of no-good yellow-bellies who should go off and
fight in France if it's a war they're after. Still, the bang from the
rifle up above in the building caught everyone off-guard and the
shocked silence of the small crowd watching as she went down
like a sack. The young fella caught between a rock and a hard
place, slipping through the door in her blood, no turning back
now. Our flag flying above it all.

Knocking. Knocking. 'Yes. Elizabeth O'Farrell. For Commandant
MacDonagh please.' Blindfolded. Headquarters: a table up

a few steps in a small room. Thomas MacDonagh a teacher alongside Pearse in St Enda's school. Poet, playwright. Here we go again. 'Orders cannot be taken from a prisoner. I, myself, am next in command. Nothing to say to the surrender. Not until I personally confer with General Lowe, the members of the provisional government already prisoners and ...'

Father Augustine. Yes. Commandant MacDonagh's conditions: An intermediary, Father. A place where they might not lose face. A request. Yes. To confirm this with James Connolly in person. And yes. I'm sure the grounds of St Patrick's Cathedral would be grand. Arranging and balancing and stepping back. General Lowe to meet Thomas MacDonagh. 3 o'clock sharp. Right so.

Only the men are left here now. Packing in silence. Afraid to catch one another's eyes. Dreading what they might see there. Numb at the prospect. Death. Penal servitude. Life in the colonies. Eily O'Hanrahan's brothers – Michael and Henry – empty out their pockets. About £3 in silver. Half shame-faced. 'For the Ma.' And another lad follows suit. 'Getting married', he says, handing me £13 in gold, 'afraid to leave it in the lodgings, like. The mot. Get it to her if you can.' A young *Cumann na mBan* woman. Saw her up in the kitchens in the GPO. Just a slip of a thing, not a pick on her, but bright as a spark with a ready smile. 'I'll do my best.'

Standing outside Jacob's, waiting. The sudden crack of gun-fire coming from inside the building. Another blast follows shortly after. Commandant Tom MacDonagh appears. Ashen. Stalks down the street with barely contained rage. One of the Tommies is trigger-happy. Opened fire on unarmed Volunteers. MacDonagh beside himself. Glaring at Captain Wheeler. 'Give the order, sir. He is shooting my men. Stop him, sir.'

Later the flag is dragged down and those left alive inside called to line up. Maps drawn with great care, passed over. 'To disclose the location of several bombs left behind, that they might be disabled. We're soldiers, sir, not bloody murderers.'

Commandant Cornelius (Con) Colbert in charge. Men and
women are clearing the hall for a céili, no notion of defeat.
Most of the week spent waiting, listening to gunfire in the
distance, making forays outside for food. Commandant Thomas
MacDonagh sent in. Gives the word. Con Colbert stunned when
it sinks in, standing in the yard, tears rolling down his cheeks.
Unconditional surrender.

Men posted in all corners of the establishment. Some refusing
to budge. Seán O'Broin being talked down from the rafters by
Annie Cooney. 'Orders are orders.' Finally flinging his rifle down
in disgust. Crestfallen. 'Is this what we've been living for all
this time?' And the word goes out. 'Anyone wishing to escape
should do so now.' A bunch of Volunteers decide to do just that,
with a *Toor-a-loo boys, I'm off.* But the *Cumann na mBan* women
are staying put. In for a penny ... Collecting in front of the fort.
Shaking the men's hands. 'God's Speed! God Bless!' Captain Rose
MacNamara it is, her voice ringing out to those women under
her command. Twenty-two of them, all told. 'We'll be giving
ourselves up with the men, whatever our fate might be.' Guns
and ammunition pass into petticoats and pockets until they're
told to hand them over or be searched on arrival. Every last one
of them to be stripped of arms and ammunition.

In the confusion before they set off, Annie Cooney spots Con
Colbert. Unaware of the package he sent to Miss Lucy Smith
stationed in the GPO, his letters to 'the loveliest girl in Dublin'.

Annie shoulders her way through the crowd. Asks for a
keepsake. 'Some souvenir, Con. Just in case, well, you know ...'
Dazed, Con looks at her and then down at his hands as if he's

never seen them before. Holds them out to her. 'Here. Have this. It's all I have.' A piece of brown bread in one hand and a sock in the other. Annie reddens. Declines. Says he might be glad of both of these things soon enough.

Nearby, Máire O'Brennan rips and crumples pages from her diary, this written over the past week inside the Distillery. A trail of incidents trampled underfoot as they march. Rather let things pass into oblivion than inadvertently incriminate some poor soul, when it's clear now that everything is to be confiscated.

Voices raised with rebel songs as the girls try to lift all their spirits or drown out their fears as they march. Competing with the insults and obscenities of those lining the pavements. Soldiers. Separation women.

Already some of the men are being taken out, shipped off to the internment camps of Frongoch in Wales. The women marched into Richmond barracks. Asked to give their word of honour. No attempts to escape, nor breaking of glass, by order of, in accordance with ...

Sunday, 30 April 1916
Dublin Castle, 7.00 pm

A guest I am, not a prisoner. On the orders of General Lowe.
A guest, who cannot leave, in the charge of a Matron, who is to
make me comfortable if you please.

Julia. Julia. Where are you, love?

A fine guest I am, waking to find I've been robbed in the night.
A medical officer it was. A downright sneak thief! Clothes.
Money. On objecting (a strenuous objection as it were), my
clothes are restored to me. Needless to say, not the money.

'Provost Marshal is it? Can you please tell me the whereabouts
of ...'
'Lock her up.'
'Am I a prisoner so?'
'Very much so, Madam.'
'Excuse me but I have been assured that ...'
'You won't be alone for long, if that's your worry.'
'Excuse me, I have General Lowe's word that I ...'
'In there.'
Doors slammed and locked.
Ship Street Barracks.
A filthy storeroom.

Back from the exercise yard: Emily and Annie Norgrove, Molly
O'Reilly, Jinny Shanahan, Helena Molony, Katie Barrett, Brigid
Davis, Dr Kathleen Lynn. What a sight for sore eyes they are.
All here from City Hall, the first garrison to fall.

Seán Connolly, Citizen's Army. No, no relation to James. Seán an actor for years at the Abbey. An old friend and colleague of Helena Molony's. Of course she wouldn't mind fighting alongside him. Mattie Connolly, Seán's younger brother, sounding the marching orders on his bugle. Setting off at a good lick from headquarters at Liberty Hall. Up Dame Street towards Dublin Castle. A voice jeering from the footpath, 'Here's the Citizen Army, with their pop-guns.' Most of them not sure where they're headed. The Angelus bells rings. And where do they think they're off to? A policeman puts out his hand. Unarmed. Shot dead by Seán Connolly. A British soldier shot by Helena Molony, before they manage to slam the gates of Dublin Castle shut on them.

Later, on the roof of City Hall, across the road from Dublin Castle. Mattie learns the sounds of the different guns and rifles. A habit of his, this attention to the sound of things. The German Mauser: a loud explosion and echo, quite distinct. The sharp crack of the Lee-Enfield, with a ring to it. The shotgun with a bark all its own. A fine bit of late evening sunshine catches them off-guard. Distant rifle firing. The occasional ping of something nearby.

All relaxing under the strain, enjoying the sight of Commander Seán Connolly hoisting the flag, rambling across the roof. A kind of crack, or so it sounded. A bit of stonework splintering nearby. A stray bullet. And Connolly lurching over onto his side, bleeding from the stomach.

Dr Kathleen Lynn crawls out towards him. Helena Molony. His head in her lap. A last act of contrition whispered into his ear. Dead. No help for it. Dearly beloved, survived by his sister and brother, Katie and Matt. Both beside him, 'Sorry, Mattie, sorry.'

The slating all around perforated with bullet holes. Cracking. Chipping. Sliding loose. The rattle of machine guns and their echo and Dr Lynn close by, talking to him now. 'Enough sniper duty for tonight, Matt.' He suddenly crying bitterly. Fifteen years of age. 'Go on down and get some rest. Go on. Off you go.' All of them tense with the weight of this building stretching out into infinity underneath them as the chill of the evening settles in. An armoured car rumbles below, chains rattling. Something is manoeuvred heavily into position. 'Matt, that's an order.'

The bugle, still slung over his shoulder bangs against the narrow stepladder as he lowers himself down off the roof. Sixteen, fifteen, fourteen men and nine women.

Helena sent to the GPO for help. One of the Citizen Army men, William Halpin, a small wiry fellow, stops her before she sets off. 'For the mot, Miss.' Gives her money. Helena slips back into City Hall again under cover of darkness. No help to be had. Inside, none of them quite sure who's in charge. A tall man no one really seems to know by the name of O'Reilly. Afraid to light a match. Pitch black. Groping around with fingers and boots for walls, stairs, rails. Shuffling of feet. Incoherent murmers. The voice of authority is that of Dr Kathleen Lynn, Chief Medical Officer of the Irish Citizens Army. Holding them firm.

In the night the building shudders, vibrates. Glass shatters. Ceramic and stucco explodes. Screams in the darkness. The edifice itself torn open, rent asunder. Machine gun bullets pour in, scoring walls and doors. A boy, in great pain, bandaged, has been seated, almost enveloped, in an old armchair. It tucked into a corner facing the wall in an effort to safeguard him. Chunks of plaster, stucco, cornices, come dislodged. Shaken loose from walls and ceilings, hurtling blindly downwards in the dark.

A British voice. Loud, deep, too close, shouts from inside the airless blackness, 'How many are here? Surrender in the name

of the King.' William Halpin, traps himself between a rock
and a hard place, hidden up the chimney for hours, breathing
poisonous fumes in the dark, the damage hard to dislodge in
later years.

Lights. Blinding. Belittling. Troops pour up the stairs. Stopping at
the sight of these girls. Citizen Army girls. Not first-aiders. Never
seen the likes of it before. Don't know what to make of it nor
who they're talking to. 'Are you hurt, ladies? How many of them
are there?' Jinny Shanahan, it is, quick as flash. 'We're grand,
but there are hundreds of them, up on the roof.' Precautions.
Procedures. Delaying the inevitable for hours. Laughing later,
though no one laughed when one of our men accidentally put
the eye on her, calling out as he was being marched away, 'Hello
there, Jinny, are you all right?' On surrendering, Dr Kathleen
Lynn announces herself: 'A Red Cross doctor and a belligerent.'

Dr Kathleen Lynn in a state of apoplexy about the range of
possible infections they're being exposed to. The stench of
over-flowing rubbish, debris and offal. The humiliation of
being sneered at by soldiers who refuse them the basic respect
of closing the privy door. Back from exercise only to be locked
again into that cramped basement room, which Dr Lynn insists,
ought only accommodate four people were it to conform to
Public Health requirements.

'Elizabeth O'Farrell. Is it yourself?' A handful of sweets, broken
bits of barmbrack from her pockets and crumbs of information.
All spread out for sharing. Meagre pickings.

Later, left to our own devices, Helena being Helena,
exchanges notes and coins through a gap in the window with
a young woman on the street up above. Trying to get fresh
undergarments sorted out, she already having spent some nights
sleeping in Liberty Hall before falling in behind Connolly.

Dried biscuits for dinner. The old guard telling us to moisten
them with water or we'll never get them down. Produces a few
oranges from his pockets. The spoils of a British raid on nearby
buildings. 'Something sweet for the ladies', says he, handing
them over.

Monday, 1 May 1916
Ship Street Barracks, 3.50 pm

'All right, ladies ...'

Everyone to be moved. A tall man in khaki with black trimmings
giving the orders. 'Sir, I ought not be a prisoner. General Lowe,
he ...' He looking at me incredulous, then laughing. 'Don't be
silly. We know for a fact you shot six policemen yesterday.'
The others wonder what I'm doing. I can see it in their eyes. But
I see no merit in being a prisoner for the sake of it, never being
one to believe in the glory of sacrifice nor martyrdom. Nor can
I see any way of helping Julia from the position of one who is
as deprived of liberty as she, if this is what has become of her.
But there's no use arguing here with this insolent bully who calls
himself a soldier.

Richmond Barracks. We all handed over to two officers. 'Excuse
me sirs, but I have General Lowe's word that ...' Now everyone
incredulous. But I must insist wherever I can. Honour and
martyrdom will simply have to accommodate themselves to the
demands of love and trust and freedom.

Out for exercise with the others and I catch sight of him
crossing the yard. 'Father Columbus!' Who had accompanied me
as I went towards the Four Courts. Feels like a lifetime ago now.
The others confused. 'What is she doing? Who does she think
she is?' Calling out across the yard. He puzzled, then surprised
to see me here. 'Yes, Father. Tell Captain Wheeler, General
Lowe.' A mistake? A promise? Trying to hold onto General
Lowe's word, this proving difficult.

'Please ask General Lowe. Is he going back on his word? Am I
to believe his word of no worth whatsoever? Tell him I will let it

be known if this is so, Father. Tell him. *Of great assistance.* Those were his words. That this may be taken into consideration ...' Some of the women witness my performance with somewhat more than mixed feelings.

All marched to Kilmainham Gaol. Marie Perolz on the side of the road. Just back from delivering her dispatches to Cork. Dismayed at the delay in catching up with her pals. Her comrades. She always in the thick of it. Herself and Nellie Gifford running a bureau for Irish lads they've managed to persuade to desert the British army. Forever collecting clothes and on the lookout for jobs for them. Dressed her little niece in a blue velvet coat and bonnet for Easter Sunday. Arriving after Sunday Mass into Liberty Hall with a basket packed to the gills with guns and ammunition. Delighted to pass the stuff over and the rest of the money too. In and out of Liberty Hall this past fortnight, pushing a pram. Full of loaves of bread and metal bits. 'Perolz', they say, 'Perolz, you're wanted.' And she's gone. Burning steady with conviction. 'Anything for Kate Houlihan!' A passionate lover of Yeats and Lady Gregory's Ireland.

It was Marie Perolz who woke us that night. Herself and her brother knocking on our door at two in the morning. Me bleary with sleep. Julia following me down the stairs. 'Dublin is Rising on Monday. Tell them.' Both of us awake in a flash, swallowing a cup of tea. A dash of water on our faces. Tucking a dampened handkerchief into my bag for the journey. 'No, No. We won't go back asleep.' Catching the first trains out of Dublin. Athenry and Galway. Carrickmacross. Planning to meet up at the GPO on our return.

Marie Perolz spent the week kicking herself. Sitting on a train stopped and stalled, held overnight, to and from the other end of the country. Wishing to bite her own tongue out, for the foolishness of having said she'd go to Cork and Macroom of all places. To have missed the whole thing, when she'd been ready and itching to take up her position alongside Mallin and the Countess. Never mind she'd given her gun to a man on the platform who looked like he knew how to handle it more than she ever would. Now looking to fall in with the march here. One of the women shaking her head. 'No sense at all in this, Perolz. What good will you be locked up? Get on out of here before you're spotted.' Almost relieved when they came pounding on her door a few days later. The Black Maria waiting outside.

Dragonheads snake in stone up above the entrance. *Sin no more lest worse shall come to thee.* This inscribed inside the gate. A few girls giggling with nerves at the sight of it. Others snorting with indignation.

Warders nervous. Such an enormous influx of inmates. Anxious that it be done as quickly as possible. Stripped. All off. Everything. Searched. Sorted. Three or four to a cell.

A confuffle out in the corridors as more of our comrades arrive. Everyone jostling, trying to stick with friends. Loved ones. Helena Molony, the Norgrove sisters, Jinny Shanahan. And Liz? Any word? Miss Elizabeth O'Farrell? Ship Street Barracks. Richmond Barracks. Helena Molony says she was with her, yes in the gaol, in her own cell, then told to come out, taken away somewhere. She didn't know where. Sighted here, there and everywhere. No one can tell exactly where she is now. Something's not right. A whiff of something unsaid. Liz, love, what have you done?

Every hour it seems more news seeps through the walls. Word of South Dublin Union ... Over five thousand of the desperate and destitute housed there. A battlefield once it started, with nowhere for them to run to. Heard Eamon Ceannt persuaded his wife Áine with her mother and their son Ronan to decamp off to Mrs Cathal Brugha's house. Out of the way of the firing line.

Another story for Nurse Margaretta Keogh. Four bullets caught her outside the workhouse, she trying to protect those in her care. A mistake they called it.

Frank Sheehy Skeffington. Mrs Julia Hughes saw him, hands
shackled behind his back, dragged into the barracks near
Portobello Bridge. His leaflets against looting drifting sodden in
the canal water below.

All of the talk here: John Hogan shot dead as he popped out
to get a bottle of milk, him insisting he couldn't drink his tea
without it. Old Mr MacKenzie, shot while sitting in his favourite
chair beside the window.

A guest of the Castle I am yet again, it would seem. Awaiting General Lowe's pleasure. He finally strides in, flushed, full of apologies, with a, 'Nurse O'Farrell! Madam! Never let it be said that I would go back on my word. My honour, Madam, must be upheld. My word.'

It would appear that Father Columbus managed to catch his ear, to pose my question: 'Was his promise to be considered worthless?' For the General is protesting. 'Isn't it clear that this is all just a terrible misunderstanding?' Without his knowledge, let alone approval. And couldn't I understand in such strenuous times how such a thing could happen? A mistake. Begging my pardon. 'No, of course. Disgraceful indeed! To be stripped and searched like a common criminal. Unthinkable. Upon my honour!'

'And the money I was holding in good faith? Stolen in the night.' Of this he professed himself entirely ignorant. 'The Provost Marshall was it? The scoundrel shall be punished. The full sum returned this instance. My apologies. Never should have happened. Never. Certainly not with my consent.'

Refusing the offer of a car, of an escort to my own front door. He furnishes me with a letter, his handwritten testimony, by which he intends to save me from any further trouble or inconvenience with the military. I am accompanied by the matron down to the Castle gate and step out into Dame Street, the city already deserted at this hour. Not a prisoner. No.

Tuesday, 2 May 1916
Kilmainham Gaol

Dr Kathleen Lynn. Diary entry: Saw MffM early this morning.
Greatest joy.

Tuesday, 2 May 1916
Kilmainham Gaol

Madeline ffrench Mullen. Diary entry: Met the Doctor going for water, had her to breakfast hip, hip.

Tuesday, 2 May 1916
Kilmainham Gaol, Recreation hour

Sixteen-hand reels and jigs and singing, much to the alarm of
the warders. So many scooped up in the general mayhem for no
apparent reason. A Miss Mulhall, seeing our *Cumann na mBan*
rounded up through the ribbons of her drapery shop, goes out to
cheer them on. Promptly arrested herself.

Another young woman previously unknown to any of us. Beside
herself with worry these past few days. Three little ones waiting
for her. Fifteen months, the youngest. And the oldest, just four
years of age. 'A minute, nothing more. A bit of water from the
pump outside.' 'No, you can't call a neighbour. No, you should
have thought of that before.' Begging the warder. A certain Miss
Barrett. A most unpleasant piece of work indeed. 'Get word to
them. Please.' Doors slammed. Pleas ignored. Bolts shot home.
Sobbing in some quarters. And a lilt and a tilt as some of the
girls sing, voices rising and falling in waves echoing through the
damp air of the cells.

Later our scratching fitful sleep is penetrated by voices.
Footsteps. Lights passing somewhere outside. It'd be three
o'clock in the morning or thereabouts. 'Our men', whisper some
of the more fanciful. 'Attacking in the night! Or maybe Germans!'

Gunshot Volleys. A groan.
Footsteps.
Grunting from the effort of dragging something between them.
Silence.

No doubt what. Just who. The beginning of the reprisals. Who knows where it will end. We lie here listening to them finishing their work. The wall's chill creeping up my hand placed flat against it. As if I could divine something else through its thickness. Feel its pulse. Where are you, Liz?

Some time during those long restless hours a piece of brown paper is slipped through a broken window into one of the women's cells. Written by a soldier, himself imprisoned there: 'Our men who are gone today ... '

Breakfast. Cocoa, dry bread and names passed as lumps of dead clay and sorrow between us.

'Padraig Pearse, Tom MacDonagh, Tom Clarke.'

Moments of confusion and a brief sighting. Constance Markievicz under armed escort in the yard, to exercise alone. Women rushing to her, pushed back out of the way, she dragged off again to solitary confinement. No contact to be had. Her influence deemed pernicious.

Banging on Mrs O'Hanrahan's door. A neighbour sticks his head
out the window. A roar: 'Shut those windows and lights or we'll
do it for you!' Eily and her sister Cis, loaded into a military lorry.
Taken to Kilmainham Gaol. Passing Mrs Tom Clarke, sister of
Ned Daly in a hallway. Her second visit here this week, the first
being for her husband, Tom.

Up heavy iron stairs, rattling down a bleak corridor to their
brother Michael's cell. Nothing in it. No light. An old bag thrown
in a corner. A bucket. Not even a bed. And Michael. Rushing
to him. No idea where Henry, fondly known as their brother
Harry, is. Michael's fear for him palpable. A table, chair, candle
brought in. To enable him settle his affairs. Books. That's all he
has. *A Swordsman of the Brigade* by Michael O'Hanrahan. *When
the Norman Came* by Michael O'Hanrahan. Now he writes his
name on paper headed *Kilmainham Gaol*. 'Books to go to Mother
and to my sisters after her death.' Love to Mother and Máire
and Harry if you manage to find him. No weeping. Not that.
Downstairs again, out of sight of her brother, Eily faints. Laid
out on a stretcher on the ground. 'After all, ladies, your brother
is getting the death he would have wished for.' A soldier's
reasoning. Poor consolation for the loss of one they hold so dear.
Passing Grace Gifford on the way out they overhear her tell
an officer, 'I am Mrs Plunkett.' Married for an hour, widowed
before the night is out. The sisters taken home in the same lorry
that brought them. The soldier asks to shake hands, offers his
deepest sympathy. The prospect of sleep. Unthinkable. Hideous.

Gunshot Volleys. A low moan. A single revolver shot. Its echo reverberates forever. Holding our breath in the silence.

Joseph Plunkett, Ned Daly, Michael O'Hanrahan, William Pearse. The news shocking when it hits. Plunkett's mother here, in their hands too. Held in her cell. Not allowed to see her son, nor officially informed of his death. And Willie Pearse. What were they thinking? Everyone knows he follows where his brother leads. Guilt by association. Shame on them.

One by one each woman is taken for interrogation. Some up to nine times in the same day. Trying to question us out of our own convictions, these growing stronger with every passing hour. Disgust breeding defiance.

'No. It was not only first-aid. No.'
'No.'
'No.'
'Yes. Orders are orders.'
'Anything I had been asked to do. Yes. Anything.'

Eily O'Hanrahan decides she can't do it. Can't tell her mother.
Her beautiful brother. Holds everything in. Sets off with her
friend Máire Byrne. Father Augustine takes one look at them.
Fetches his coat. Parlour doors. Gently clicked shut. Mrs
O'Hanrahan. Tea, Father. Crockery, spoons, nerves rattling.
'Something to tell you, Mrs O'Hanrahan. Eily asked that I ... '
Breaks the news of her son Michael's death. Execution. Then the
floodgates open. Tidal waves of grief.

Word gets out, sweeps down the houses. Time to pay respects.
The house full of mourning and mounting fury. Endless cups of
tea. May God have mercy on his soul. May God help us avenge it.

Another knock on the door. One of countless. Standing down the
few stone steps. Nurse Elizabeth O'Farrell. 'So sorry Eily. Heard
about it this morning. Brought this. Promised them I would. For
your mother. From Michael and Harry.' £3 in change. Tightly
knotted together in a handkerchief.

Friday, 5 May 1919
Kilmainham Gaol

One volley in the night.
John MacBride.
Cocoa, dry bread, silence.

Mass in the small prison chapel. Women seated on wooden pews in the gallery above. Creaking, straining, craning to see the men below. Kneeling in the front seat. Eamon Ceannt. Body of Christ. Michael Mallin. Body of Christ. Sean Heuston. Body of Christ. Body of Christ. Con Colbert looks up at the whispering. Spots Annie Cooney. Waves back. Shakes his head in farewell. Cornelius Colbert. Dead the next morning.

Readying ourselves for another long night. Sleeping in our
clothes this past two weeks. All of us crawling with God knows
what, despite our best efforts to eradicate what Dr Lynn terms
'our intruders'. With that there's a bit of a commotion outside.
Keys jingling. Clanking. Doors pulled open. All women to
assemble in the main courtyard. All in a state of great tension,
wondering what our fate is to be. And where. One of the officers
smirks, 'Off to Jamaica to pick oranges with the lot of you! The
boat is due to sail.'

A louder voice calls for order. I can barely concentrate as he
begins to rattle off names quick-fire, caught between his accent
and mispronunciations and repetitions as he guesses as to the
actual written name so that the strain of listening out for my
own causes me to grow light-headed. Not quite clear where he
procured this list as there is a perplexed silence to the call for
some of our members who clearly are not amongst us, having
slipped the net at an earlier stage of the proceedings.

MrsKathleenBarrettMissEibhlinBarryMissBrigidBradyMiss
MarthaBrownMissEileenByrneMissWinnieByrneMissMary
ByrneMissChristinaCaffreyMissMayCarronMissBrigidCarron
MissMayCooneyMissAnneCooneyMissLilyCooneyMissEileen
CooneyMissMarcella CosgroveMissEllenEnnisMissBrigid
DavisMissMayDerhamMissMayGahanMissMayGalvinMiss
BrigidGoughMissJuliaGrenanMissRose HackettMissBridget
HegartyMissMollyHylandMrsAnnieKellyMissBessieKellyMiss
JosephineKellyMissKatieKellyMissLily ThompsonMiss
MargaretKennedyMissBridieKennyMissMaryLawlorMiss
CatherineListonMissMaryListonMissBessie LynchMiss
BrigidLyonsMissKathleenMaherMissBridgetMastersonMiss

JosieMcGowanMissRoseMcGuinnessMissBrigidMurnaneMiss
RoseMcNamaraMissAgnesMcNameeMissMayMoloneyMiss
Florence MeadeMissJennyMilnerMissCarrieMitchellMiss
AnneWiselyMiss PaulineMorkanMissRoseMullallyMiss
MargaretMartinMissM.MulhallMissMaryMurrayMissBrigid
MurtaghMissEmilyNorgroveMrsAnnieNorgroveMissChristine
DoyleMissLilyO'BrennanMissMaireO'BrennanMrsAnnie
O'CarrollMrsMaryO'CarrollMissNoraO'DalyMissMargaret
O'FlahertyMissSheilaO'HanlonMissMollyO'HanlonMissEmily
O'KeefeMissJosieO'KeefeMissMollieO'ReillyMissMollie
O'SullivanMissDorothyO'SullivanMissJosephinePurfieldMiss
PriscillaQuigleyMissMariaQuigleyMissJennieShanahanMrs
JosephineSpicerMissMaryStephensonMissKathleenWalsh

'All of you ladies whose names have been called out are free
to leave on the condition that you behave yourselves in the
future.' This despite the curfew in place. To run the risk of being
arrested again or wait till morning. Some of the younger ones set
off, only to find themselves stopped at the gates. 'Upon further
consideration. For your own protection. Another night will do
you no harm now will it?' Huddling crestfallen. Six or seven to a
cell, like forlorn sparrows, waiting for the first light of morning
that will finally spring their cages.

Bridget Foley steps up. 'There must be some mistake. My name.'
'No, there is no mistake. Step back Madam. Your name is not on
my list.' Others similarly detained. Dr Kathleen Lynn, Helena
Molony, Countess Plunkett, Winifred Carney, Nellie Gifford, Kit
and Nell Ryan, Annie Higgins, Marie Perolz.

However, for the more mature ladies, Father McCarthy, although
by no means sympathetic, he would like to be clear, will escort
those who decide to take their chances, across the barricades.
No further than that, mind. After which each person proceeds at
her own risk. A British Tommy volunteers to go along. To keep
them out of harm's way.

Alone now. The city all but unrecognizable. Battered. Deserted. Just cats. Prowling and peering from the bedraggled shrubbery around Merrion Square. Can't remember so many of them. Silent as death. Their stealth renders the tramp of my boots all the louder. My footsteps bounce against closed doors, blinded windows. Resounding, rebounding, I'm sure every stray shadow will accost me, call on me to halt. Curtains in tatters. Cracked stonework, rubble, weeds. A huge rat scuttles out of a broken wall, we both startled by the encounter. Time to buck up the pace a bit.

Passing the last block of buildings, a shadow looms. Another set of feet fall in time with my own. At first I think I'm hearing things, imagining it. Blood rushing in my ears. And then there's no question of a doubt. A silhouette looms. And I'm jumping over cracks, tearing down the blackened street, my voice raised, racing ahead of me, 'Elizabeth O'Farrell, what do you think you're up to? Are you trying to give me a heart attack?'

In the Summer of 1916, a group of women, all of whom took part in the earlier Rising, met and were photographed in the garden of Ely O'Carroll's house in Peter's Place, Dublin.

Standing on the left: Anne Tobin, Aoife Taafe, Marcella Cosgrave, Kathleen Murphy, Bridget Foley.

Standing on the right: M. Kelly, Máire Nic Shiubhlaigh, Lily O'Brennan, Elizabeth O'Farrell, Nora O'Daly, Mary Murray.

Front Row: Madeline ffrench Mullen, Miss Eileen Foley, Dr Kathleen Lynn.

Second Row: Rose McNamara, Kathleen Kenny, Margaret Walsh, Mrs Mary Lawless, Jenny Milner, Eileen Walsh, K. Kennedy, May Byrne, Eileen Cooney, Annie Cooney.
Third Row: Mary Moore, Kathleen Lane, Sarah Kealy, Gertie Colley, Mary O'Hanrahan, Anne Wisely, Bridget Murtagh, Priscilla Quigley, Julia Grenan, Stasia Twoomey, Brigid Walsh.

Fourth Row: Nora Thornton, Rose Mulally, Sheila O'Hanlon, Maria Quigley, Margaret O'Flaherty, Josie McGowan, Eileen Cooney, Josie O'Keefe.

Fifth Row: Lucy Smith, Nora Foley, Pauline Morecombe, Dolly Sullivan, M. Elliot, Mary Sullivan, Tilley Simpson, Catherine Treston.

Back Row: M. Kelly, Brigid Brady, Jinny Shanahan, Kathleen Barrett, Rosie Hackett, Margaret Ryan, Brigid Davis, Chris Caffrey, Patricia Hoey.

Common Intellectual series

Current Editions

Future Editions

For future editions, please visit the Copy Press website

Copy Press is committed to bringing readers and writers together and invites you to join its Reader's Union – please visit www.copypress.co.uk